I dedicate this book to my mom, who instilled in me a passion for reading, writing, and education from an early age. Also, to my twin sister's dog, Beau, whose humorous personality helped inspire this story.

www.mascotbooks.com

Passing The Bone: America's Next POTUS

For more information, please contact:
Mascot Books
560 Herndon Parkway #120
Herndon, VA 20170
info@mascotbooks.com

Library of Congress Control Number: 2015917446

CPSIA Code: PRT1215A
ISBN-13: 978-1-63177-316-7

Printed in the United States

PASSING THE BONE
AMERICA'S NEXT
POTUS

by **Heather Patterson**

Illustrated by **Jingo de la Rosa**

Fellow canines of this great nation, it is my honor to address you from the White House for the final time.

Since April 14, 2009, it has been my privilege to serve as POTUS, Pup Of The United States! I have fought *tirelessly* for frequent doggy play dates, both foreign and domestic. All dogs deserve to play with one another, regardless of their training, breed, and personal opinion of cats.

I have crossed enemy territory to befriend my foes and have taken to heart the task of making peace with international dignitary pets. I am also pleased to say the felines of DC and I are now on speaking terms!

As I prepare to leave my role as First Pup, it would be unpatriotic of me to depart this honored position without preparing the next White House Pup. Like the President, there will be qualifications every dog will have to meet.

If you want to be the White House Pup, you must be able to sit, stay, and come for your master. In order for the animal population to follow your paw prints, you must earn it!

The Pup Of The United States must be born in the U.S.A. and be patriotic. You should make a practice of stopping when you see the American flag. Show your respect with an exaggerated tail wag or a paw over your heart. Additionally, it would be wise to learn the tune of "The Star Spangled Banner" and bark along accordingly!

Many times, you will get to ride in a helicopter with the President and land on the South Lawn. Only the president lands on the South Lawn, so it is VERY important to act presidential while you exit the helicopter. The yard is wide and spacious, and the lush grass is tempting, but this is NOT the time to run around, chase your tail, or frolic about like a silly puppy. Hold your head high, smile, and put one paw in front of the other. Show the nation you can walk across the South Lawn with pride!

As you make your way from the South Lawn to the White House, a United States Marine will open the door for you; scratching the door is not necessary. Actually, there will be no need to scratch ANY doors. It's called the *White* House for a reason, so let's keep it that way.

Every pup wishing to be POTUS must know showing respect and honor to our armed forces is vital! Never forget to show your thanks! When the President is given a salute, stop, look at the serviceman, raise your paw, and salute back.

The White House Pup must also be able to travel long distances by air, land, and sea. I can't tell you how many hours I've flown on Air Force One cooped up in a little room. Tempting as it may be, you may not run around Air Force One like it's your personal backyard. As POTUS, you represent the most prestigious family in the world, so act like it.

Should you accompany the President to Camp David, know this: swimming in the pool is strictly for the President! However, if you earn the First Lady's favor, she might let you splash around in a lukewarm bath before bedtime. (I cannot confirm or deny a stash of rubber bones in the bathroom cabinet!)

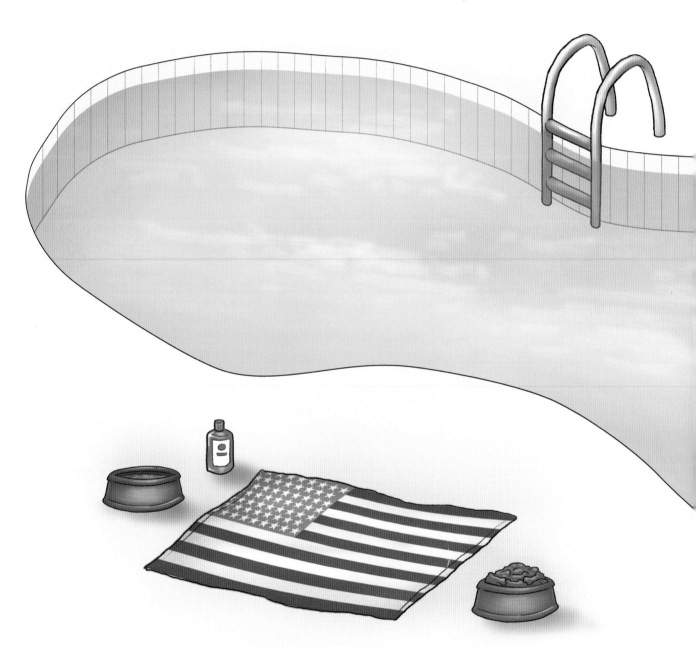

Traveling certainly has its perks, and I have more information that will really make your tail wag. As a reward for good behavior, you might be able to meet your favorite talk show or late night TV host! But remember, talk is business as always. The issues of the country must always be on your mind! Use any celebrity platform to praise the homeland! Congratulate the rise of tourism on behalf of the cats of New York City. Or represent our interest in global affairs by sending warm wishes to the Chief Mouser to the Cabinet Office, our friendly ally across the pond.

The White House will welcome many world leaders. Some of these guests will be presidents, prime ministers, kings, queens, princes, or princesses. You MUST be able to greet these special guests with respect. Excessive barking, licking, jumping, and parading around like a puppy are strictly prohibited! You do NOT want to get taken out back by a Secret Service agent.

Miss Beazley Bush

Mr. Barney Bush

Speaking of the Secret Service, learning to keep a secret is key. Many times in the Oval Office, I heard security briefings, important meetings, and top-secret missions. Your duty is to honor and protect the United States. Our species is known for loyalty and you must live up to it! All requests for top-secret information by outsiders must be met with silence.

Often, the White House Chef will prepare a delicious formal meal for the First Family, staff, and guests. If you clear your bowl every time, he might slip you leftovers from the banquet table in the kitchen room. (You can thank Barney Bush and Miss Beazley for that tidbit. This is of course, off the record.)

Try your best to train yourself to a strict bathroom schedule. It is just too distracting to interrupt the President's day by doing your business. It goes without saying, but NO ACCIDENTS IN THE WHITE HOUSE.

Candidates, the President never has a day off and neither will you. You might be used to sleeping for most of the day, but from the moment you step into the White House, you can kiss your napping days goodbye. Occasionally, the Chief of Staff might excuse you from a meeting. You may use this unexpected free time to nap in the Lincoln Room, but don't count on it happening often.

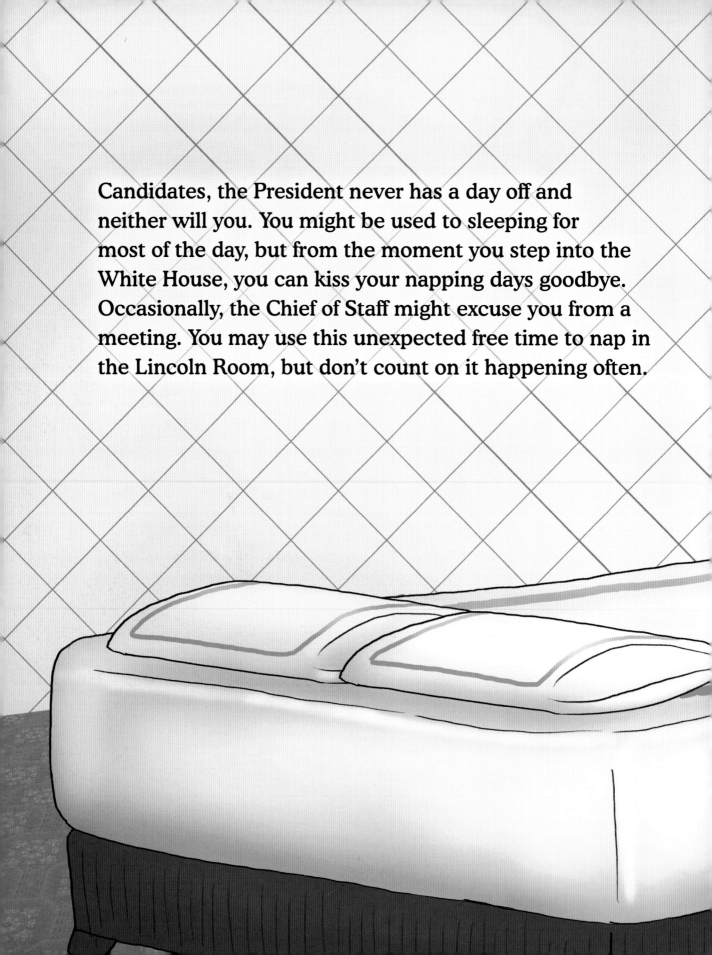

In closing, canines of this magnificent country, it has been my honor to serve you the past several years. As my term comes to an end, I look forward to backyard runs, mud splashing, chewing bones in public, and playing fetch at the doggy park alongside you citizens.

It is with honor I will pass the bone to the next Pup Of The United States. I have full confidence the future POTUS will represent the land of the free and home of the brave with pride, honor, and loyalty. For God and Country!

Barking off,
Bo Obama, POTUS
(Pup Of The United States)

P.S. – As tradition for the next POTUS, I have taken the liberty of hiding a bone as a welcome gift in the White House! The First Lady gave specific instructions to the Secret Service not to remove it, should they find it. (They are VERY good at spotting things.) Happy hunting!

About the Author

Heather Patterson is a debut children's author
and elementary school teacher in Dallas, Texas.
Passionate about children, education, and
politics, Heather wrote this book for young
readers to relate to current events and develop
a love for American history.